A play by Jeanne Willis

Illustrated by Dave Neale

Characters

Dad – Mr Smith

Jo – daughter

Mum – Mrs Smith

Jack – son

Krang I –
alien narrator

Krang 2 –
alien narrator

The year is 2080. On Planet Krang, two Krangs are listening in to a conversation on Earth, using their powerful telescope and sound detectors.

Krang I: Oooh, look! The Smiths are planning a family holiday.

Mum:	I fancy going to Spain this year.
Dad:	Spain? No, it's too hot.
Jo:	How about Greenland, Dad?
Dad:	Greenland's too cold!
Jack:	We always spend holidays on this planet. How about a trip to Mars instead?

Krang 2: It's not impossible, you know. They have got a rocket in the garden.

Jo: Oh, yes! Let's go to Mars!

Dad: It's a long journey, kids.

Mum: But our neighbours next door went to Mars last year.

Dad: Funny how we never saw them again.

Jack: Please let's go, Dad!

Jo: It will be fantastic!

Dad: Okay. Pack your bags. We are going to Mars!

7

Krang I: Yes! They've decided! They are climbing aboard their rocket.

Dad: Five ... Four ...

Mum: Three ...

Jo: Two ...

Jack: One ...

Krang 2: Blast off! They are on their way.

Krang 1: They are shooting through space at the speed of light.

Jo: Are we there yet?

Mum: No, Jo.

Jack: I'm bored.

Dad: I told you it was a long way.

Mum: Let's have a sing-song, shall we?

Jo: Do we have to?

Dad: (*singing*) Off on holiday we go, yo-ho-ho, yo-ho-ho!

Jack: Dad, that's an awful racket!

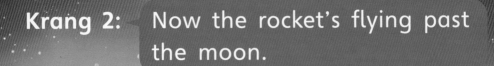

Krang 2: Now the rocket's flying past the moon.

Krang 1: It's zooming through an asteroid belt.

Jo: Are we there yet, Dad?

Dad: It's not far now.

Mum: We should be there in ten days.

Jack: Ten days? I wish I'd brought a book.

Krang 1: The rocket's flying past Venus.

Krang 2: They are going the wrong way if they want to get to Mars!

Jo:	We could play "I Spy".
Jack:	There's nothing to spy!
Jo:	Yes, there is. I spy something beginning with B.
Mum:	Bag?
Jo:	No.
Jack:	Bubble gum?
Jo:	No ... black hole. Look out, Dad!
Mum:	Brake, dear!
Dad:	Too late. Hang on to your hats!
Krang 1:	Oh no! The rocket's vanishing into the black hole!
Krang 2:	Hang on – now it's whooshing out the other end.

Jack: Where are we, Dad?

Jo: Is this Mars?

Mum: Mars doesn't look like this on the postcards.

Dad: Let me check the map.

Krang 1: It's not Mars. It's Planet Krang.

Krang 2: Look – just over there! Mr Smith's parking the rocket.

Jo: Let me out!

Jack: I'm starving.

Mum: I wonder where the shops are.

Dad: Let's go and eat.
            Forward march!

Krang 1: They've gone! Now's our chance!

Krang 2: Yes – let's get into their rocket!

Krang 1: Five, four, three, two, one ...

Krang 2: Blast off!

later

Mum: Where's our rocket?

Dad: I'm sure I parked it here.

Jack: How are we going to get back, Dad?

Mum: I knew we should have gone to Spain!

Krang 1: Look, there's Earth! We are coming in to land.

Krang 2: Yes! Touchdown – in the Smiths' back garden!

Krang 1: We've only come for a holiday.

Krang 2: But if we like it, we might just stay!